Things I Can Do

Written by Keytorial Hilliard and McConnell Faure Jr.
Illustrated by QBN Studios

To the little one I love the most,
Thank you for making me a mother,
your mother ❤

I can bounce bounce bounce.

I can sing sing sing

La

I can clap clap clap.
Can you do all those things?

e
f
g

I can giggle giggle giggle.

I can run run run.

I can play play play.
Can you do all those things?

2
1
3
4

Let (all) bounce bounce bounce,
and have fun on all accounts.

Lets (all) sing sing sing,
and fill the world with big adream.

Lets all clap clap clap,
McConnell's running on his last lap.

Lets all giggle giggle giggle,
while we watch the fish wiggle.

Lets run run run,
to see who number one

Lets play play play,
and do it all again the next day.

CPSIA information can be obtained
at www.ICGtesting.com
Printed in the USA
LVHW070318181021
700713LV00005B/9

9 780578 992662